Turn It Down!

There are roadworks outside Witherbottom Hall. The noise is terrible, with **pneumatic** drills and heavy machinery. Sir Ralph Witherbottom is getting very frustrated by the noise. Isabella has turned on her CD player and her music is deafening!

"Isabella! Please will you turn down that noise! I can't hear myself think!" called Sir Ralph.

"Oh, dad! Don't be a killjoy…!" groaned Isabella. "We all make noise! I hear you talking on the phone in the study when I'm in my bedroom! That old car of yours makes a terrible din, too!"

Max, the butler, came in, clattering teacups and saucers. "See! Even Max is noisy!" laughed Isabella.

"What is an annoying 'noise' to one person may be enjoyable to someone else," said Max. "But some sounds can actually be so loud that they damage your ears!"

"That's right, Max. Sound is measured in **decibels**, Izzy. The more decibels there are, the louder the noise. That drill out there is creating about 100 decibels. Max's vacuum cleaner makes about 70 decibels, and when I wheel the lawnmower round outside, I'm blasting my ears with 90 decibels! That's why I wear ear protectors," said Sir Ralph.

"I like the tuneful whistling of the kettle – but that makes 50 decibels!" laughed Max. "And that old fridge of ours hums at 40 decibels!"

"Usually we're quite lucky here, but constant **noise pollution** can disturb sleep, cause stress and affect concentration. It can even cause hearing loss!" said Sir Ralph.

Dad's music – now that's noise pollution!

How loud?

Match the correct noise level to each object.

1 50 decibels

2 70 decibels

3 90 decibels

4 40 decibels

5 100 decibels

Top Tips

Noise pollution can include barking dogs, parties, house and car alarms, local factory noise and traffic noise. Think about your neighbours before you make lots of noise!

Did you know?

Over half of the homes in England and Wales are experiencing noise levels louder than the **World Health Organization's** recommended daytime level of 55 decibels. The world is also getting noisier. The number of people who have reported hearing annoying noise from their homes has gone up dramatically in the last ten years.

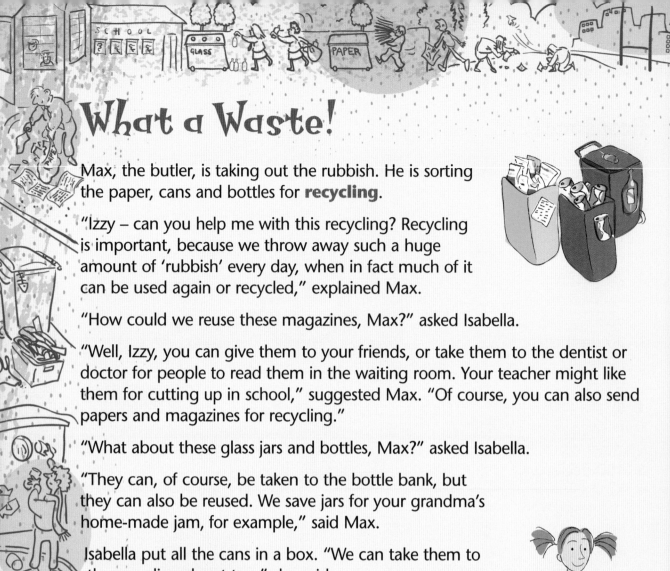

What a Waste!

Max, the butler, is taking out the rubbish. He is sorting the paper, cans and bottles for **recycling**.

"Izzy – can you help me with this recycling? Recycling is important, because we throw away such a huge amount of 'rubbish' every day, when in fact much of it can be used again or recycled," explained Max.

"How could we reuse these magazines, Max?" asked Isabella.

"Well, Izzy, you can give them to your friends, or take them to the dentist or doctor for people to read them in the waiting room. Your teacher might like them for cutting up in school," suggested Max. "Of course, you can also send papers and magazines for recycling."

"What about these glass jars and bottles, Max?" asked Isabella.

"They can, of course, be taken to the bottle bank, but they can also be reused. We save jars for your grandma's home-made jam, for example," said Max.

Isabella put all the cans in a box. "We can take them to the recycling depot too," she said.

"You could also sort out some old toys and clothes to take to the charity shop, Izzy," said Sir Ralph, "or chop up any old cotton T-shirts and woollen jumpers that can't be reused and put them on the compost heap with vegetable peelings and grass clippings! But remember to ask me first!"

"Reusing and recycling saves energy and so makes less **pollution**. This means there is less rubbish to fill landfill sites. Recycling one glass bottle saves enough energy to power a TV for over an hour!"

What? I'm reusing!

"Well, then – after we've sorted out this lot I reckon I can watch TV all day!" said Isabella.

Crossword

Complete the crossword.

Across:

2 You can take your old toys to this kind of shop
3 Using something again
4 You can save these bags after you go shopping

Down:

1 Where you recycle old bottles and jars
2 You can put these on the compost heap
5 When you don't recycle things they end up in these sites

Top Tips!

Charity shops are places where people can buy cheap second-hand things and the money they spend goes straight to charity. They are also places where people can get rid of the things they no longer need – so everybody wins!

Did you know?

You can reuse lots of things – plastic carrier bags for more shopping or for bin liners; margarine tubs for storage; yogurt pots for growing seeds; and plastic bottles can be cut in half and used to cover plants, to protect them from slugs and snails.

A Wildlife Haven

Isabella wants to make a wildlife garden. She has been researching what to do on the Internet and in books.

"Max, I've made a list of the things wildlife need: food, water, **shelter** and places to breed. Now all I need to do is decide how to provide them!" said Isabella.

"The birds already have water from the bird bath and food on the bird table. You could add a bird box for them to nest in once the weather warms up," suggested Max.

Some wildlife I could do without!

"I've got a pattern for making a bird box and plenty of scrap wood in the garage," said Sir Ralph Witherbottom. "So that's one thing sorted out already! We'll have to be careful to position the nest boxes to make sure the birds move in!"

"Why don't you make a ladybird house, too? If you drill holes in a branch and cover the end with a 'roof', it'll give the ladybirds somewhere to **hibernate** in the winter," said Max. "We could put it in the vegetable patch and the ladybirds could get rid of the greenfly!"

"Great! I've got designs for making homes for toads, newts, bats and hedgehogs too. I'm also going to make houses for lots of bugs – mason bees, bumblebees, lacewings and stag beetles," said Isabella.

"Well, here's some presents to get you started, Izzy – some seeds to grow flowers that will attract butterflies, moths, bees and hoverflies; and a buddleia bush too – butterflies love them!"

Wordsearch

Find these words.

Wildlife

Shelter

Food

Winter

Nest box

Bird

f	y	g	f	t	b	i	r	d	l	w
w	o	d	s	x	c	a	r	t	g	i
r	l	o	u	n	m	o	p	q	w	n
e	d	r	d	g	y	h	t	r	b	t
t	j	u	h	n	k	g	f	d	n	e
l	o	n	e	s	t	b	o	x	d	r
e	f	t	g	h	y	n	b	v	c	f
h	d	e	f	i	l	d	l	i	w	e
s	x	c	f	h	i	o	l	p	k	h

Plant **annual** flowers such as the 'poached egg plant' – they grow quickly and attract insects.

Did you know?

You can make a hedgehog shelter by piling up dry leaves and twigs in a corner of the garden. Prop a sheet of wood over the top to keep the rain off. Bundle together hollowed stems and bamboo canes to make homes for beetles. Log and stone piles with lots of 'nooks and crannies' will encourage lots of different wildlife into the garden.

Revise Time

1 Fiii in the missing words, using the words in the box to help you.

> decibels   parties   pneumatic   traffic   drill   loud   disturb   noise

a _____ noises can damage your ears.

b Sound is measured in _____.

c A _____ _____ creates 100 decibels of sound.

d Loud sounds can be called _____ pollution.

e Constant noise pollution can _____ sleep.

f Noise pollution can include _____ and _____.

2 True or false? Write 'T' for true and 'F' for false in the boxes.

a Noise pollution can help you sleep. ☐

b Loud sounds can damage your ears. ☐

c Sound is not measured in decibels. ☐

d The vacuum cleaner creates 10 decibels of noise. ☐

e Barking dogs and car alarms are noise pollution. ☐

f The more decibels there are, the greater the noise. ☐

3 Fill in the missing letters to make words to do with recycling.

a R _ _ b _ sh

b Cha _ _ _ y s _ _ p

c _ ars

d L _ _ _ _ ill

e P _ _ _ uti _ _

f B _ _ _ le b _ _ ks

4 Think of at least one way to reuse each item on the list.

a Glass jars _____

b Plastic bottles _____

c Plastic bags _____

d Magazines _____

e Toys _____

f Clothes _____

5 Circle the correct word(s) in each sentence.

a Animals do/do not need shelter.

b Ladybirds hibernate/fly through the winter.

c Butterflies love/hate buddleia.

d You have to position bird boxes carefully to make sure birds move in/stay out.

e Flowers/mud will attract bees and hoverflies.

f You can help hedgehogs by building/moving their shelters.

6 Answer these questions about wildlife.

a Describe hibernation. _____

_____

b Name an animal that hibernates. _____

c What can you do to help birds feed? _____

d Name a plant butterflies love. _____

e Name something ladybirds eat. _____

f When do birds use birdboxes? _____

_____

11

Settle Down!

"I wish you'd settle!"

Isabella, Max and Sir Ralph have gone for a walk in the countryside. They have stopped on a hill. "What a view! Look at that town there, by the river. Doesn't it look like a wonderful **settlement**?" said Sir Ralph.

"What's a settlement?" asked Isabella.

"Settlements are places where people live and work, Izzy. A farm, a village, a town or even a city," explained Sir Ralph. "Most of these places have developed over hundreds of years. Early settlements developed into the villages, towns and cities of today."

"Why do you think people decided to settle here, in this place?" asked Isabella.

"Well, as you can see, the settlement is near a river, so there's a water supply. There's plenty of flat land, for growing food and building houses, and the hills behind the settlement protect it from bad weather. It's also possible that the largest hill over there had a castle built on it, for **defence**. Look, you can see the ruins of a large building," said Sir Ralph.

"In this country, many early settlements were built at the bottom of south-facing hill slopes. That's because it was more sheltered," said Max.

"Settlements needed wood for fuel, so people could build, cook and heat their homes – so a forest or wood nearby was a real benefit. People might also need stone for building, so a **source** nearby would make building a settlement easier and more likely," added Sir Ralph.

"Amazing!" said Isabella. "And there was me thinking they built the town here just because it was pretty!"

Draw a settlement

Draw your own village settlement. Include a hill, a lake and some houses; or any other features you can think of! Draw **symbols** on the **key** that match the ones you use on your map, to explain what the features are.

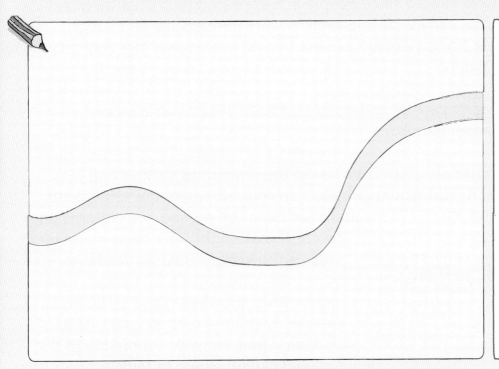

Key

Hill:

Lake:

Houses:

Top Tips

You could use mapping or **graphics** software to create a copy of your map.

Did you know?

Place names can give you clues about why or how settlements developed. For example, names that end in 'borough' or 'bury' – coming from the Anglo-Saxon word for 'fortified place' – would have been well defended against an attack. Place names ending in 'toft' or 'thwaite' – coming from the Viking word for 'clearing' – would have been built on flat, clear ground.

Evidently So

Sir Ralph has taken Isabella to the museum, to look at what **evidence** there is of early **settlements**.

"Settlements have existed since people first appeared on the earth, Izzy! The caves that the earliest people lived in were perhaps the first settlements. Ever since, people have left behind evidence of the way they lived," said Sir Ralph.

"Are the remains of palaces and great buildings the only evidence of settlements?" asked Isabella.

"Not at all! **Archaeologists** have found the remains of villages and farmsteads too. **Aerial photographs** can suggest where the settlements would have been, by picking out patterns on the earth that might have been made by walls or buildings," said Sir Ralph.

> I wish Izzy would leave behind a bit less evidence!

"Of course, knowing where settlements were likely to be – such as near water, wood and stone supplies – would help the archaeologists know where to look, I suppose?" said Isabella.

"That's quite right, Izzy. In some places, other clues are available. It's thought that places such as Durham, where there was an important place of worship or church like Durham Cathedral, may have helped to attract people – and even traders – to a site. **Pilgrimages** to these places were very important and this may have caused the development of settlements that would then develop into towns," said Sir Ralph.

"It's amazing, isn't it? I did wonder how people decided where to build a town. It makes sense that they grow over time, where the conditions are right," said Isabella.

Crack the code

The letters of the alphabet have been matched to a number.

A	B	C	D	E	F	G	H	I	J	K	L	M	N	O	P	Q	R	S	T	U	V	W	X	Y	Z
1	2	3	4	5	6	7	8	9	10	11	12	13	14	15	16	17	18	19	20	21	22	23	24	25	26

Decode the following numbers back to letters to find the words.

1 19, 5, 20, 20, 12, 5, 13, 5, 14, 20   _____

2 4, 5, 22, 5, 12, 15, 16, 13, 5, 14, 20   _____

3 16, 9, 12, 7, 18, 9, 13, 1, 7, 5   _____

4 5, 22, 9, 4, 5, 14, 3, 5   _____

5 13, 21, 19, 5, 21, 13   _____

6 4, 21, 18, 8, 1, 13   _____

Top Tips

Find out about sites people visited on pilgrimages –
there may be one close to you!

Did you know?

Artefacts found at archaeological dig sites can tell us a lot about early
settlements. The remains of grain and food stores can tell us the sorts
of crops people grew and the animals they kept. The remains of
spindles and **looms** can tell us that sheep were kept for wool, or that
flax was grown, for instance.

Growing Up!

Isabella, Max and Sir Ralph are in the city for the day.

"Is the city a settlement, dad?" asked Isabella.

"It is, Izzy. The size of settlements can be very different. There are **hamlets** – just tiny places, really, with a few houses, but no shops. Villages are a little bigger. They have some services, such as local stores, a school, a pub, a church and possibly a post office," said Sir Ralph.

"Towns are bigger still, Izzy," said Max. "They have all the things villages have, but they also have supermarkets and a train station. Cities are even bigger. They have all the things villages and towns have, but they also have a hospital, a cathedral, a large shopping centre, a sports stadium and a university."

"There are more of the smaller settlements than the larger ones, Izzy," said Sir Ralph. "Of course, there are many different types of settlement. Many of the earliest settlements were defensive – for protection from attack. Market towns grew, as farmers needed somewhere to buy and sell crops and animals. **Industrial** towns developed near factories and industries that needed lots of workers, such as coal mines or cotton mills."

Brighton or Blackpool – who cares? They both have rock!

"There are also **port** towns, which grew in areas where ships brought goods into the country and sent them out of the country, like Southampton," said Max.

"Don't forget holiday **resorts**, like Brighton and Blackpool! They're my favourites!" laughed Isabella.

Match them up

Draw a line matching the settlement to its **facilities**. Careful – some facilities are part of more than one type of settlement!

Town	Village	City

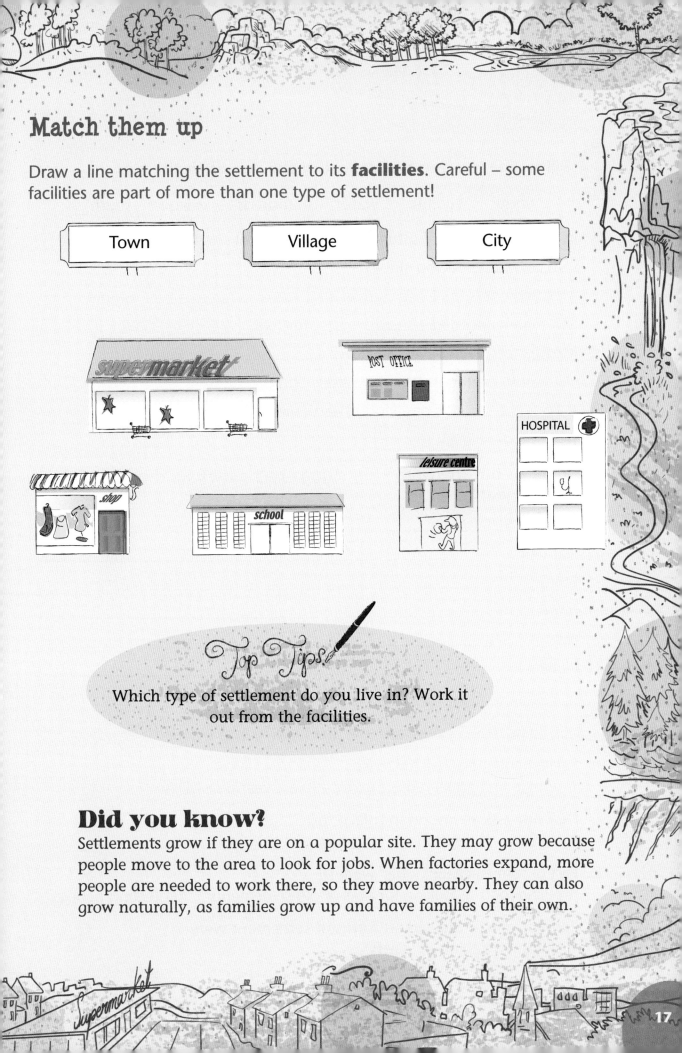

Top Tips

Which type of settlement do you live in? Work it out from the facilities.

Did you know?

Settlements grow if they are on a popular site. They may grow because people move to the area to look for jobs. When factories expand, more people are needed to work there, so they move nearby. They can also grow naturally, as families grow up and have families of their own.

Revise Time

1 Fill in the missing words, using the words in the box.

| wood | weather | water | hundreds | village | south |

a In this country many settlements were built at the bottom of _____-facing slopes.

b A settlement is built near a river so it has a _____ supply.

c Settlements needed _____ for fuel.

d Most places have developed over _____ of years.

e Hills could protect settlements from bad _____.

f A _____ is one kind of settlement.

2 Why would the following things be needed at the site of a settlement?

a A river _____

b Flat land _____

c Stone _____

d A forest _____

e Hills _____

f Rich soil _____

3 Choose the correct answer and write the letter in the box.

a Settlements have existed since:
A people first appeared on earth B last year C 1818

b Durham was an important place for:
A trading B fighting C worship

c Part of some archaeologists' work is:
A selling food B looking for sites of old settlements C protecting people.

d Perhaps one of the earliest forms of settlement were:
A caves B cabins C flats

4 True or false? Write 'T' for true and 'F' for false in the boxes.

a All evidence left behind is of great buildings and palaces. ☐

b Settlements are likely to be near water supplies. ☐

c Pilgrimages stopped settlements from developing. ☐

d Aerial photographs can suggest where old settlements were. ☐

e Early settlements have developed into villages, towns and cities. ☐

f Durham is not an ancient settlement. ☐

5 Answer the following questions.

a Put these places in order of size, from smallest to largest: City, Hamlet, Town, and Village.

_____

b What did industrial towns develop near?

_____

c Name two things that a town would have that a village would not.

_____

d What are settlements that are protected from attacks called?

_____

e Name something that you could find in a city, but not in a town.

_____

f What can cause settlements to grow naturally?

_____

6 Match these anagrams to the correct word.

a wotn   b mhleat   c dfneeisev   d illgeav   e tiyc   f dirlauntsi

village   industrial   hamlet   defensive   town   city

All About India

Sir Ralph has received a letter from a friend in India, who is the head teacher of a school in Bangalore.

"Look, Izzy! Here's a letter from my friend Prem – he's sent a photo of his family. It's come all the way from India – look at the stamp!" said Sir Ralph.

"That's great, dad. I know it's a long way, but where exactly is India?" asked Isabella.

"It's a beautiful country in south Asia, Izzy. Get the **globe** out and I'll show you," said Sir Ralph.

Isabella fetched the globe from the study. "Here it is, Izzy. It's that country there – it's almost diamond-shaped. This is the Indian Ocean, around the bottom of the country, and that tiny island just off the bottom is called Sri Lanka," said Sir Ralph. "Can you see which countries share a **border** with India, Izzy?"

"Erm…" said Isabella, spinning the globe gently, "Pakistan… China… Nepal… and Bangladesh!"

"Now, can you remember how to use an atlas? If you wanted to find India – what would you do?" asked Sir Ralph.

"I'd look in the country listings at the front. I could look for India in that list, or I could look in the contents list for Asia. To find a place in India, I'd look in the index at the back. It's in alphabetical order," said Isabella.

"That's excellent, Izzy! You do listen to me sometimes!" laughed Sir Ralph.

Where's Timbuktu then?!

Label the map

Look at the map of India and label it by filling in the boxes. Use an atlas or globe or the Internet to help you.

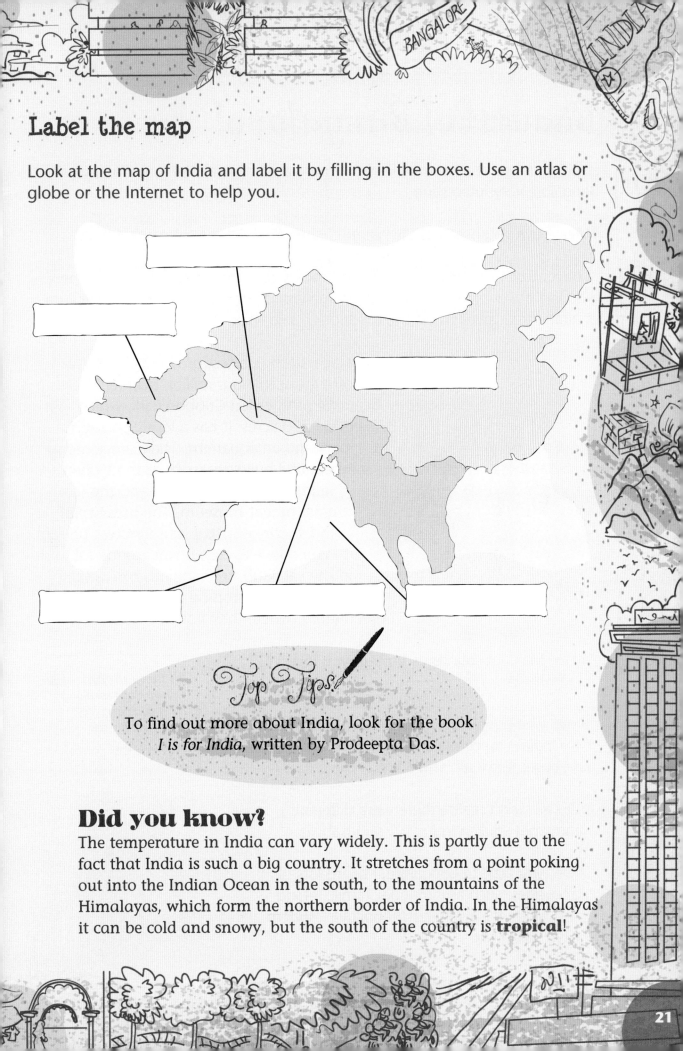

Top Tips!

To find out more about India, look for the book
I is for India, written by Prodeepta Das.

Did you know?

The temperature in India can vary widely. This is partly due to the fact that India is such a big country. It stretches from a point poking out into the Indian Ocean in the south, to the mountains of the Himalayas, which form the northern border of India. In the Himalayas it can be cold and snowy, but the south of the country is **tropical**!

Beautiful Bangalore!

Isabella looked at a book to find out more about India. She found a city called Bangalore very interesting.

"Max, have you heard of Bangalore?" she asked. "It looks beautiful!"

"I have, Izzy. I visited that city when I took a gap year after college. The people who live there call it 'the best city in the world', or 'the garden city', because of all the trees planted on the roadsides," said Max.

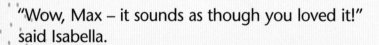

"It's an amazing place. It's the fastest growing city in Asia and is home to nearly four million people! There's a beautiful park, called Cubbon Park, which covers 500 acres. It has a lovely children's park and an aquarium. There are some beautiful buildings, such as the Vidhan Saudha, the public library and the government museum. The **industrial** and **technological** museum was brilliant – you'd love it, Izzy. It was wonderful to sit in the Lal Bagh, the fabulous **botanical gardens**, full of tropical plants, with a lovely greenhouse, where they hold flower shows."

"Wow, Max – it sounds as though you loved it!" said Isabella.

"I did. The people are great and come from all over India. You can hear so many different languages spoken!" said Max.

"Oh – I didn't realise there were different languages spoken in India," said Isabella.

"Oh, yes, Izzy! In Bangalore, I heard lots of languages, such as Kannada, Tamil, Telugu and Hindi. It's a very cosmopolitan, modern city!" said Max.

It's like at the park – you hear dogs speaking poodle, collie, Jack Russell...

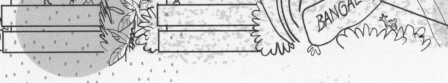

Wordsearch

Find these words.

- Hindi
- Lal Bagh
- Bangalore
- Cubbon
- Garden city
- Museum
- Aquarium

a	d	f	g	h	h	j	t	v	f	b
h	h	b	l	a	l	b	a	g	h	a
e	r	i	y	n	b	v	q	h	h	n
r	r	h	n	o	b	b	u	c	t	g
t	t	r	u	d	h	k	a	l	e	a
d	c	t	y	b	i	j	r	k	s	l
g	a	r	d	e	n	c	i	t	y	o
r	h	a	f	h	k	j	u	o	n	r
o	s	m	u	s	e	u	m	i	m	e

Look for Bangalore in an atlas. What can you find out about the city and the people who live there?

Did you know?

Bangalore has many beautiful buildings. The Bangalore Palace, built in the 1880s, was inspired by Windsor Castle, in England! King Chamaraja Wodeyar saw Windsor Castle during a trip to England and wanted to build something just like it back home.

Fantastic Photos

Max is showing Isabella photographs from a trip he took to Bangalore when he was a student.

"The colours in these photographs are so strong and bright," said Isabella. "There's lots of building work going on though, Max! Look at all these building sites!"

"Bangalore was full of **construction** projects when I was there, Izzy. Apartments and houses were being built at an incredibly fast rate. Some people live in group housing projects, instead of houses that are just for one family. Some of the houses were very close together! In some places, it felt as though you could stretch your arms out of the window and touch your neighbour's house! It's a strange feeling… but it still wasn't as built up as Bombay, when I stayed there for a few days," said Max.

"Max, you're so lucky! I'd love to travel like you have!" sighed Isabella.

"I'm sure you will, Izzy, but be prepared to 'rough it' a bit! Travelling to faraway places can mean you stay in conditions that aren't like they are at home. The roads in Bangalore are rather poor and the transport isn't as reliable as it is here, but a city transport system with an additional fleet of buses is being created – that should make a difference!"

Yup, things can get pretty rough round here too sometimes…

"Well, having to 'rough it' abroad sounds like more fun than all the homework I have to do here!" laughed Isabella.

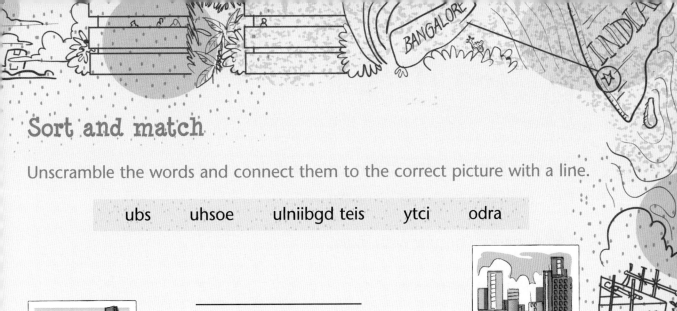

Sort and match

Unscramble the words and connect them to the correct picture with a line.

ubs   uhsoe   ulniibgd teis   ytci   odra

_____

_____

_____

_____

_____

Top Tips!

Look in the tables at the back of the newspaper, or on the Internet, to find out what the temperature is in Bangalore.

Did you know?

India has a **population** of one billion (one thousand million) – but then it is a very large country! It has the second biggest population in the world, after China, and more than three times the population of the United States of America. Amongst all those people, an amazing seventeen major languages are spoken in India – with an incredible 844 **dialects**!

Revise Time

1 True or false? Write 'T' for true and 'F' for false in the boxes.

a   The ocean around India is the Atlantic. □

b   China shares a border with India. □

c   India is in southern Asia. □

d   India is almost a square shape. □

e   The island at the bottom of India is called Sri Lanka. □

f   England is on the border of India. □

2 Fill in the missing letters.

a   I _ _ ia

b   I _ di _ n   O _ _ an

c   S _ _ th   A _ _ a

d   N _ p _ l

e   S _ _   L _ _ ka

f   Pa _ _ st _ n

3 Answer the following questions about Bangalore.

a   How many people live in Bangalore? _____

b   What do the people who live there call it? _____

c   Name two languages spoken there. _____

d   What is the big park called? _____

e   How big is the park? _____

f   What is the Lal Bagh? _____

4 Draw a line matching the name to what it is.

a Bangalore   b Lal Bagh   c Cubbon   d Vidhan Saudha   e Telugu

Public library   Botanical gardens   Park   Language   City

5 Fill in the missing words, using the words in the box.

reliable   houses   created   construction   built   group

a Some people live in _____ housing projects.

b The transport is not as _____ as it is here.

c A city transport system is being _____.

d Some _____ are very close together.

e Houses and apartments are _____ very quickly.

f There has been a great deal of _____ in Bangalore.

6 Answer these questions about Bangalore.

a Are the houses in Bangalore far apart or close together?

_____

b What do some people live in, instead of a house for only one family?

_____

c What is being created to improve the transport?

_____

d How are the roads in Bangalore different to those in England?

_____

e What did you feel you could do if you stretched your arms out of the window in the house?

_____

27

Tropical Chembakolli

Isabella wanted to find out more about India, so Sir Ralph took her to a photography exhibition in the town centre. It was about a village in the south of India, called Chembakolli. It is in a hilly, heavily forested area of Tamil Nadu, set into the Nilgiri Hills.

"Oh, dad! These photographs are breathtaking! It looks so beautiful and peaceful. I didn't know that India had areas of **rainforest**. Look at those leaves! They're such a gorgeous, deep green," said Isabella.

"Yes, Chembakolli is truly beautiful. It looks like paradise. The village is in the middle of the rainforest and the nearest settlement is several kilometres away. It's called Kanjijolly," said Sir Ralph.

These fellas are bad enough – but a tarantula? Yuck!'

"It looks very peaceful. I love the way the animals of the forest are so close to the village. The tiny tree frogs are fabulous! The orang-utans are amazing too, and the lovely jaguars – imagine seeing creatures like that, without going to the zoo! It would be heavenly," sighed Isabella.

"True, Izzy – and there are only around one hundred families living there. But you'd have to deal with hairy-legged tarantulas and poisonous snakes, too!" said Sir Ralph.

"I think I'd put up with them for a chance of seeing one of these huge blue butterflies or a flock of parrots flying overhead!" laughed Isabella.

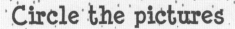

Circle the pictures

Circle the things you might see near Chembakolli village.

Top Tips!

Look for the goods at the supermarket labelled
fair trade, produced by people in villages
like Chembakolli.

Did you know?

Rainforests are in danger from people cutting and burning down the forests, to make room for houses and the farming of herds of cattle for beef. The rainforests are important for the whole world, because the trees help to put oxygen into the air and we need oxygen to breathe. Many medicines have been developed using plants found there too. Of course, threatening the forests also endangers the animals – and the people who live there.

The Grass is Always Greener...

Isabella bought a **CD-ROM** about Chembakolli to show Max. When she got home, she loaded it onto her computer and showed him.

"It says that in Chembakolli, most families all live together in one house – grandparents included! It doesn't feel crowded, though, because each house is about twenty metres from the next, so there's a lot of space. Each home has its own area of rainforest too," said Isabella. "Can you imagine having a rainforest as your garden? How marvellous!"

"Sounds wonderful, doesn't it, Izzy? It also says that the villagers spend most of their time outside, because it's so warm – and that's for most of the year! I like the look of those long benches outside the houses, with porches to keep the hot sun at bay!" said Max.

Without TV I'd miss all the nature shows... but then I suppose I'd be seeing a live one!

"Look at this, Max – the CD-ROM says that many people choose to sleep outside. How incredible, to fall asleep with the noises of the forest all around you!" said Isabella.

"I think I'd prefer to be indoors, away from all those biting bugs and spiders!" shuddered Max.

"Well, some people do sleep inside. It's also where food is cooked and water is kept, in great pots next to the fireplace. The villagers fetch water and carry it from a **source** ten minutes' walk away. The water isn't very clean, but there are no fresh water pipes leading to the village," said Isabella.

"That sounds like hard work, but what would be harder for you would be the lack of electricity. That means no computer, and no TV!" laughed Max.

Chembakolli or British village?

Match the descriptions to the correct place with a line.

1 Grandparents live with the family.

4 Water carried to the house.

2 Water piped to the house.

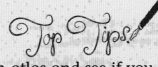

Chembakolli

British village

5 Houses 20m apart.

6

3 NO TV!

7 Grandparents mostly do not live with families.

Top Tips!
Look at an atlas and see if you can find other countries where it would be warm enough to sleep outside all year round.

Did you know?

In many parts of India, grandparents live with the family in the same house. This is the case in many parts of the world. In Britain, this also happened in the past, but less so now. In India, the older members of the family are looked after and they help the household to work efficiently by looking after children and helping to do jobs around the house.

House and Home

Sir Ralph found a website that gave a **virtual tour** of a house in Chembakolli village. That means that someone had taken photographs inside a house and loaded the film onto a website, so people could imagine they were actually in the house.

"These houses are bigger inside than you might expect, Izzy," said Sir Ralph. "Some of the houses only have one room, but others have two or three rooms. The houses seem quite dark, even during the day, as there's no electricity, but I think they look rather cosy!"

"This is an interesting web page, dad. It shows how the houses are actually built. They aren't made from red bricks or stone, like many of the houses in Britain. They don't have **slate** roofs either," said Isabella.

"Well, if you think about it, houses are usually built from local materials. In Chembakolli, there aren't great stocks of stone. Their local materials are wood and mud, so that's what they use," said Sir Ralph. "The huts are built slowly. First a wooden frame is built, then mud is used to build up the walls. Walls are built in small layers, because each layer has to dry in the sun before another can be made. The roofs are made out of local straw, called **foodar**."

"But, dad, how can a wall made from mud be strong?" asked Isabella. "Surely they just crumble?"

"Not at all, Izzy! Look at these pictures. They bake hard in the sun; as hard as stone. The walls last for many years," said Sir Ralph.

"Right – I'm off to experiment with mud in the garden!" said Isabella. "I may be some time!"

Wait, Izzy!
I'll help!

Which one?

Put the materials used to build houses into the correct column.

Britain   **Chembakolli**

_____   _____

_____   _____

_____   _____

Stone

Foodar

Wood

Slate

Bricks

Mud

Try to build a small model wall
from mud. See if it really does go
hard when it dries.

Did you know?

When the walls are the right height, the roof's frame is built. Plastic
sheets are draped over the frame to keep the rain out and a thick
rooftop cover is made from foodar (a dried local plant). During the
monsoon season, the rainfall can be very high, so it is important that
the material is closely woven and watertight.

Revise Time

a Chembakolli is a city. ☐

b Chembakolli is in the rainforest. ☐

c 1000 families live there. ☐

d The nearest settlement is called Kanjijolly. ☐

e Chembakolli is set in the Nilgiri Hills. ☐

f You can find tree frogs in Chembakolli. ☐

2 Fill in the missing letters to find words relating to an Indian village.

a K _ _ _ ijolly

b Ta _ _ _ _ ula

c Ta _ _ l N _ _ u

d Ch _ _ _ akol _ _

e Ja _ _ ar

f Rain _ _ _ _ _ t

3 Circle the correct word in each sentence.

a Most families in Chembakolli live together/separately.

b There are no water jugs/pipes in Chembakolli.

c Villagers spend most of their time working/playing.

d The village is without electricity/houses.

e The water is not very dirty/clean.

f Each home has its own area of rainforest/meadow.

4 Work out these anagrams and match them to the correct word.

a treaw   b eetcrliyict   c fronarites   d lliresgva   e mohes   f dsuiteo

electricity   homes   water   villagers   outside   rainforest

5 Answer these questions.

a How many rooms do houses in Chembakolli have? _____

b Are the houses built quickly or slowly? _____

c What materials are used to make the walls? _____

d How long can the walls last for? _____

e What is foodar? _____

f Do houses in Chembakolli have electricity? _____

6 Describe the process of making a house in Chembakolli.

_____

_____

_____

Draw a house from Chembakolli.

Work It!

Max came into the kitchen with a bag of shopping. He pulled rice, onions, peppers, tomatoes and oranges out of his bag and put them on the table.

"Hey, Izzy! I think Max has been shopping in Chembakolli village!" laughed Sir Ralph. Max looked puzzled.

"Most of the villagers in Chembakolli are farmers," said Sir Ralph. "They grow rice, onions, peppers, tomatoes and oranges – the contents of your shopping bag! This food is produced to feed their families, rather than to sell at the market. Some wild growing food is collected in the forest, too. They do grow some **crops** to sell though, such as coffee and tea, which they take to sell in a town called Gudalur once a year. It's the only way for them to earn money. They swap crops with the nearby village of Kanjijolly too."

"Life sounds hard though, dad. The women have to carry water, which is heavy – I know that from when I help you to water the garden. They also have to grind rice, cook food, work in the fields – and clean! After that, wood has to be collected for the fire," said Isabella.

I think life HERE is hard, too!

"The women and the older children also have to take care of the babies and toddlers, at the same time as doing all that work. Hard work, isn't it?" said Max.

"It makes life here look easy!" agreed Isabella.

Chembakolli crossword

Complete the crossword.

Across:

3 They sell crops here

4 They can trade crops here

6 They grow this to sell

Down:

1 Something to put shopping in

2 They grow these in Chembakolli

5 Red fruit, grown in Chembakolli and in British greenhouses!

Top Tips!

Research what crops are grown in the UK and find out how they are different to the crops grown in Chembakolli.

Did you know?

Many foods we eat today were originally found in rainforests around the world. Many nuts, such as brazil nuts and coconuts, and fruits such as **mangoes**, **guavas**, **papayas** and **figs** are grown in the rainforest. The rainforest is also home to fruits we know less well, like the **blue quandong**; a bizarre fruit, which looks like a big, bright blue plum!

Wild Things!

Isabella, Sir Ralph and Max have gone on a day trip to the zoo. Isabella is interested in the animals that live in the rainforest around Chembakolli.

They visited the jaguar enclosure. "They're so gorgeous, dad," said Isabella.

"I wouldn't like one of them to sneak up on me when I was gardening though, Izzy! Have you seen the size of their teeth and claws?" laughed Sir Ralph.

Next, they went to look in the bird house. "Just imagine seeing **flocks** of those parrots and budgies sitting outside your house. Wouldn't it be wonderful?" said Max.

"Yes, but just imagine the size of the bird table you'd need!" giggled Isabella.

What a strange looking creature!

They went to look at the elephants.

"In Chembakolli, the villagers have to be careful not to grow food that will attract wild animals. Elephants are a particular danger, because they can crush entire homes! Elephants are very common in the forests around Chembakolli," said Sir Ralph.

The snake house was next. Isabella and a **reticulated python** stared at each other. "I wouldn't like to find one of these chaps in my bedroom!" shivered Isabella.

"To be fair, I don't think they'd like to be in your room either, what with the piles of CDs and books and the mess – not to mention your smelly socks!" said Max.

Draw the animals

Draw and label four creatures you would find around Chembakolli village.

Top Tips

Make a collage of rainforest animals by cutting pictures out of magazines. Find out how many of them are found in the rainforest around Chembakolli.

Did you know?

The villagers' crops are in constant danger of being stolen by elephants. They can grow coconuts and papaya in safety, because they grow high up in the trees where the elephants cannot reach them. The sweet potatoes are another matter though, as the elephants love to root around in the soil for them. The farmers have a hut where they keep watch for any wild animals that may creep out of the forest to steal their crops.

Comparing Lives

Isabella is writing a report for her school newspaper, comparing life in a village in Britain to life in Chembakolli. She has been surprised at how very different they are.

"Max, I'm trying to decide what the main **similarities** and differences are between life in an English village and Chembakolli. There are so many, it's hard to know where to start!" said Isabella.

"Well, let's think about it together," said Max. "Then we can make a list."

"The houses are different – we have builders to build our homes and they're made from materials like brick, stone or glass, whereas the houses in Chembakolli are made more simply from wood and mud," said Isabella.

"Don't forget how hard everybody works. We work hard here too, but we don't have to grow all of our food ourselves, or collect heavy water in great big containers," said Max.

"We can't spend most of our time outside in this country all year round, because it's too cold!" shivered Isabella. "In Chembakolli, it's even warm enough to sleep outside – wow!"

"Our wildlife is a little different to the wildlife found in the rainforest, too!" chuckled Sir Ralph as he looked at a squirrel climbing a tree in the garden. "In Chembakolli, that would probably be a jaguar climbing the tree – or an orang-utan!"

"We'd be in danger of elephants rampaging through the vegetable patch, and our greenhouse would be history!" laughed Isabella.

Pigeons or slugs, fine – but elephants?

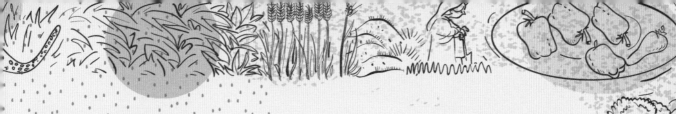

Which place?

Connect each object to the correct place with a line.

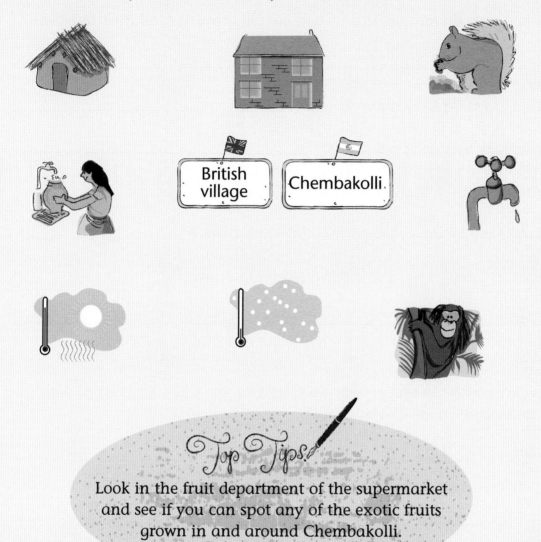

British village

Chembakolli

Top Tips!
Look in the fruit department of the supermarket and see if you can spot any of the exotic fruits grown in and around Chembakolli.

Did you know?

The climate in Chembakolli is **tropical**, which means it is warm all year round. However, there is a lot of rainfall, so the ground stays damp and plants grow to be large and luxurious. In Britain, the climate is temperate. That means we have seasonal changes, with hot and cold weather. Tropical plants cannot survive here, because of the cold, unless grown as houseplants.

Revise Time

1 **Answer these questions about farming in Chembakolli.**

a What crops do farmers from Chembakolli grow to feed their families?

_____

b What crops do they grow to sell? _____

c Where do they sell their crops? _____

d Where can they trade their crops? _____

e How many times a year do they sell their crops? _____

f Who do the women and older children look after?

_____

2 **Unscramble these words to find the names of some of the crops grown in Chembakolli.**

a epsprep _____   d focefe _____

b cire _____   e nosion _____

c ate _____   f rogaens _____

3 **Fill in the missing letters to find words to do with Chembakolli wildlife.**

a S _ _ ke   d P _ _ _ ot

b Ele _ _ _ nt   e Cla _ _

c Wi_ _ ani _ _ _ _ _   f Da _ _ er

4 Answer the following questions about animals in Chembakolli.

a Name a snake that lives in the forest near Chembakolli.

_____

b Why shouldn't the farmers grow crops that attract wild animals?

_____

c Name one animal that is particularly dangerous. _____

d Why is this animal particularly dangerous? _____

e Name a bird that lives near Chembakolli. _____

5 Circle the correct word(s) in each sentence.

a Britain is warmer/colder than Chembakolli.

b People from Chembakolli grow their own food/animals.

c British people usually buy/sell their own food.

d People in Britain build their homes from mud/stone.

e Many animals live in the rainforest/woods around Chembakolli.

f Homes in Chembakolli have/do not have electricity.

6 Fill in the missing words, using the words in the box.

| outside | rainforest | water | grow | mud | wildlife |

a Homes in Chembakolli are made from wood and _____.

b Some people in Chembakolli sleep _____.

c There are no _____ pipes in Chembakolli.

d Chembakolli is in the _____.

e People in Chembakolli _____ their own food.

f The _____ in Britain and Chembakolli is different.

Glossary

aerial photograph photograph taken from the sky or from space

annual something that happens every year

archaeologist a person who looks for evidence of life in the past

blue quandong a bizarre fruit from Australia, which looks like a big, bright blue plum

border the line where two countries meet

botanical to do with plants

botanical gardens place where collections of plants may be visited and enjoyed

CD-ROM multi media storage disk

construction when new building work is carried out

crops plants grown by farmers

decibels sound is measured in these units

defence protection

dialect the form of a language that is used in a particular area of the country

evidence proof

facilities a place planned for a particular activity – a sports facility could be a sports centre, for example

fair trade goods that are bought and sold fairly – the seller gets a fair price for the goods

figs fruit with sweet dark flesh and lots of seeds

flax a plant that is used to make the fabric called linen

flocks group of animals

foodar a material like straw or reeds, used for thatching roofs

globe round model of the earth, with a map of the countries and oceans

graphics charts, maps, drawings etc. found in books, magazines and computer programmes

guavas green tropical fruit with pinkish flesh

hamlets very small settlements, smaller than a village

hibernate a special deep 'sleep' an animal can use to save energy in winter

industrial to do with industry, such as factories

key (on a map) a box that shows what the symbols on a map mean

loom a machine used for weaving thread into cloth

mangoes green skinned tropical fruit with orange flesh

monsoon the rainy season; happens in tropical areas and results in high rainfall

noise pollution noise that interferes with everyday life (traffic noise could be noise pollution)

northern hemisphere the top half of the earth, above the equator

papayas yellowy-green skinned tropical fruit with orange flesh

pilgrimages journeys to special (often religious) places

pneumatic powered by air

pollution poisons, waste etc. that make the air, water etc. dirty and difficult to live in

population the total number of people living in a place

port a place where ships can anchor, load and unload

rainforest forest or jungle in a tropical area that is hot and wet all year

recycling processing materials that are to be used again (such as paper, glass and cans collected at recycling centres)

resorts places people go to on holiday

reticulated python a beautiful, large snake found in Asia; it kills prey by crushing

settlement a place where people have decided to live, such as a town or village

shelter a place to keep safe, away from the weather

similarities things that make one thing look like another thing

slate fine-grained rock used for roofing

source the origin or cause of something

southern hemisphere the bottom half of the earth, under the equator

spindles rods that thread is twisted and wound around upon as it is spun

symbol a picture or thing that represents (stands for) something else

technological to do with technology; the application of science to practical purposes, e.g. the building of computers, TVs and other electrical or digital products

tropical hot and humid; like the conditions found near the equator

virtual tour A tour made by computer, it seems real, because it is made up from photographs and you interact with it by moving buttons or keys

World Health Organization a group that makes recommendations about health and staying well

Answers

c As bin liners or for more shopping
d To be cut up or taken to waiting rooms
e Charity shops
f Charity shops or compost heaps

Exercise 5
a Do
b Hibernate
c Love
d Move in
e Flowers
f Building

Exercise 6
a Hibernation is when something sleeps through the winter
b Hedgehog, ladybird, etc.
c Put food out for them
d Buddleia
e Greenfly
f In the spring; when the weather warms up

Page 5
1 Kettle
2 Vacuum Cleaner
3 Lawnmower
4 Fridge
5 Drill

Page 7

Across
2 Charity
3 Reuse
4 Plastic

Down
1 Bottle bank
2 Clothes
5 Landfill

Page 9

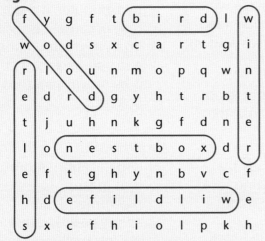

Pages 10–11 Revision exercises

Exercise 1
a Loud
b Decibels
c Pneumatic drill
d Noise
e Disturb
f Traffic, parties

Exercise 2
a F
b T
c F
d F
e T
f T

Exercise 3
a Rubbish
b Charity shop
c Cars
d Landfill
e Pollution
f Bottle banks

Exercise 4
Many answers are acceptable. Here are some examples.
a To put home-made jam in
b Plastic bottles can be cut to cover plants

Page 13
A correctly drawn settlement including a hill, a lake, and some houses
It must also have a correct key

Page 15
1 Settlement
2 Development
3 Pilgrimage
4 Evidence
5 Museum
6 Durham

Page 17
Town: school, post office, shop and supermarket
Village: post office, shop, school
City: all of the places

Pages 18–19 Revision exercises

Exercise 1
a South
b Water
c Wood
d Hundreds
e Weather
f Village

Exercise 2
a As a water supply and to travel by boat for trading
b For growing food and building houses on
c For building
d For fuel
e For protection against weather and as a defence
f For growing crops

Exercise 3
a A
b C
c B
d A

Exercise 4

a F   d T
b T   e T
c F   f F

Exercise 5

a Hamlet, village, town, city
b Factories and industries and a supply of raw materials such as coal etc. needed to make a product
c Supermarket and train stations
d Defensive or fortified
e Hospital, cathedral, large shopping centre, sports centre or university are all correct
f Familes grow up and have families of their own and new people move to the area

Exercise 6

a Town   d Village
b Hamlet   e City
c Defensive   f Industrial

Page 21

Page 23

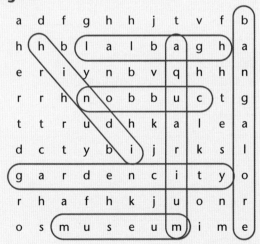

Page 25

ubs – bus
uhsoe – house
ulniibgd teis – building site
ytci – city
odra – road

Pages 26–27 Revision exercises

Exercise 1

a F   d F
b T   e T
c T   f F

Exercise 2

a India   d Nepal
b Indian Ocean   e Sri Lanka
c South Asia   f Pakistan

Exercise 3

a Nearly 4 million people
b Either 'the best city in the world' or 'the garden city'
c Any 2 of the following: Kannada, Tamil, Telugu, Hindi
d Cubbon Park
e 500 acres
f Botanical gardens

Exercise 4

a City   d Public library
b Botanical gardens   e Language
c Park

Exercise 5

a Group   d Houses
b Reliable   e Built
c Created   f Construction

Exercise 6

a Close together
b Group housing projects
c A city transport system, with an additional fleet of buses
d They are in poor repair
e Touch your neighbour's house

Page 29

Circle: jaguar, snakes, tarantula and parrot

Page 31

Chembakolli: 1, 3, 4, 5
British village: 2, 6, 7

Page 33

Britain: Bricks, stone and slate
Chembakolli: Mud, wood and foodar

Pages 34–35 Revision exercises

Exercise 1
a F	d T
b T	e T
c F	f T

Exercise 2
a Kanjijolly	d Chembakolli
b Tarantula	e Jaguar
c Tamil Nadu	f Rainforest

Exercise 3
a Together	d Electricity
b Pipes	e Clean
c Working	f Rainforest

Exercise 4
a Water	d Villagers
b Electricity	e Homes
c Rainforest	f Outside

Exercise 5
a One, two or three	d Many years
b Slowly	e Local straw
c Mud on a wooden frame	f No

Exercise 6
A variety of answers are correct. One example is: First a wooden frame is built and then mud slowly builds up the walls. Straw is then used for the roof.
An appropriately drawn picture

Page 37

Across	Down
3 Gudalur	1 Bag
4 Kanjijolly	2 Oranges
6 Coffee	5 Tomatoes

Page 39

Drawings of four appropriate creatures such as: a jaguar, a parrot, a budgie, an elephant, a python, an orang-utan, a tree frog, a tarantula and a butterfly

Page 41

British village: brick house, squirrel, tap and cold weather
Chembakolli: mud house, orang-utan, warm weather, Indian girl collecting water

Pages 42–43 Revision exercises

Exercise 1
a Rice, peppers, tomatoes, oranges and onions
b Coffee and tea
c Gudalur
d Kanjijolly
e Once
f Babies and toddlers

Exercise 2
a Peppers	d Coffee
b Rice	e Onions
c Tea	f Oranges

Exercise 3
a Snake	d Parrot
b Elephant	e Claws
c Wild animals	f Danger

Exercise 4
a Reticulated python
b Because the wild animals will eat and destroy the crops and they may be dangerous to people
c Elephant
d Because they can crush entire homes
e Parrot or budgie

Exercise 5
a Colder	d Stone
b Food	e Rainforest
c Buy	f Do not have

Exercise 6
a Mud	d Rainforest
b Outside	e Grow
c Water	f Wildlife